SPRING #1
BORN AGAIN

DOUBLE TAKE

$2.50   SODINI | FLYNN | HELLER | SANTACRUZ | GREENBAUM

D1515063

1960's Premiers

	TV SHOWS	HIT MOVIES	TOP SINGLES
1960	The Flintstones The Andy Griffith Show My Three Sons	Spartacus Psycho Exodus	Theme from A Summer Place He'll Have to Go
1961	The Dick Van Dyke Show ABC's Wide World of Sports The Avengers	The Gun of Navarone West Side Story El Cid	Tossin' and Turnin I Fall to Pieces Michael
1962	The Jetsons The Beverly Hillbillies Tonight Show: Johnny Carson	Lawernce of Arabia The Longest Day In Search of the Castaways	Stranger on the Shore I Can't Stop Loving You Mashed Potato Time
1963	Doctor Who General Hospital Let's Make a Deal	Cleopatra How the West Was Won It's a Mad, Mad, Mad, Mad, World	Sugar Shack Surfin' U.S.A. The End of the World
1964	The Addams Family Gilligan's Island Jeopardy!	Mary Poppins Goldfinger My Fair Lady	I Want to Hold Your Hand She Loves You Hello, Dolly!
1965	I Dream of Jeannie Get Smart Hogan's Heroes	The Sound of Music Thunderball Dr. Zhivago	Wooly Bully I Can't Help Myself Satisfaction
1966	Batman Mission: Impossible Star Trek	The Bible: In the Beginning Hawaii Who's Afraid of Virginia Woolf	Ballad of the Green Berets Cherish Soul and Inspiration
1967	The Smothers Brothers The Newlywed Game The Prisoner	The Graduate The Jungle Book Doctor Dolittle	To Sir With Love The Letter Ode to Billie Joe
1968	Hawaii Five-O The Mod Squad 60 Minutes	Rosemary's Baby 2001: A Space Odyssey Planet of the Apes	Hey Jude Love is Blue Honey
1969	Sesame Street The Brady Bunch Monty Python's Flying Circus	Easy Rider Midnight Cowboy Butch Cassidy and the Sundance Kid	Sugar, Sugar Aquarius I Can't Get Next to You

"I've been trying to eat more vegans."

STORY
BILL JEMAS

SCRIPT
JENN SODINI
JOHN FLYNN
BILL JEMAS

LAYOUTS
YOUNG HELLER
KURT TIEDE

PENCILS
DERLIS SANTACRUZ

COLORS
MARTA MARTINEZ

COVER
FEDERICA MANFREDI

LETTERS
CHARLOTTE GREENBAUM

EDITOR
CHARLOTTE GREENBAUM

DOUBLE TAKE

RICHARD BROOKS | PRODUCTION ASSISTANT

MICHAEL COAST | STORY EDITOR

CLAIRE DRANGINIS | PRODUCTION COORDINATOR

CAROLINE FLANAGAN | PRODUCTION ASSISTANT

ALLISON GADSDEN | EDITORIAL INTERN

WILLIAM GRAVES | DIGITAL PRODUCTION ARTIST

CHARLOTTE GREENBAUM | EDITORIAL ASSISTANT

YOUNG HELLER | STORYBOARD ILLUSTRATOR

BILL JEMAS | GENERAL MANAGER

ELYSIA LIANG | EDITORIAL ASSISTANT

ROBERT MEYERS | MANAGING EDITOR

JULIAN ROWE | STORYBOARD ILLUSTRATOR

LILLIAN TAN | BUSINESS MANAGER

GABE YOCUM | SALES & MARKETING COORDINATOR

Spring #1. September 2015. Published by Double Take, LLC, a subsidiary of Take-Two Interactive Software, Inc. Office of publication: 38 W. 39 Street, 2nd Floor, New York, NY 10018. ©2015 Take-Two Interactive Software, Inc. All Rights Reserved. Printed in Canada.

The stairs had clear doors, the bottom was a basement.

And then all the way across the garage—

—there was a laundry room.

testing...back on...we're back on the air— *ZPFZ*

—taking place in villages—

—in villages, cities, and rural homes across the country—

Can you survive the zombie apocalypse?

Yes? You probably think you can.
There is only one way to find out.
Play the **Dead Reign® RPG**. The core rule book, a ew players, some dice and an active imagination are ll you need to start playing. Rules are easy. Character reation is fast and fun. Combat, quick and deadly. urvival? Harder than you may think.

• **7 different types of zombies. Zombie combat nd survival tips.**

• **6 Apocalyptic Character Classes and Ordinary eople.**

• **101 Random Scenarios, Encounters, Settings nd places of note.**

• **100 Random Corpse Searches, other tables, eapons & vehicles.**

• **Death Cults, their Priests, power over zombies nd goals.**

• **Quick Roll Character Creation tables (10 inutes).**

• **5 sourcebooks provide more types of zombies, urvival tips, new dangers and adventure.**

• **The Dead Reign™ core rule book is 224 pages Cat. No. 230. A complete role-playing game book.**

iscover the Palladium Books® RPG Megaverse®
Fun to read. A blast to play. The Palladium role-aying rule system is the same in every game. This eans once readers become familiar with one game, ey can play them *ALL*.
Better yet, you can link and combine several game orlds to create epic, multi-dimensional adventures on cosmic scale!

What's that? You've never seen a role-playing game? The role-playing core rule book contains all the rules and data you need to create characters and get you started. Each game or supplement is a magazine size soft-bound or hardcover book, 48-352 pages, and jam-packed with great art, heroes, villains, adventures and tons of ideas. **Dead Reign®** and **Robotech®** are excellent for those of you new to pen and paper RPGs.

Rifts® is the Earth of the future, but a transformed and alien Earth where magic and technology coexist and realities from countless dimensions collide. Alien predators and supernatural monsters prey upon the human survivors and threaten to conquer the world.

Players can be any number of aliens, mutants, warriors, cyborgs, robots and wizards. Lines of magic crisscross the Earth, giving life to dragons, godlings and supernatural horrors. They also lead to dimensional gateways called "Rifts" that link the Earth to the infinite Megaverse®. In **Rifts®** anything is possible.

Unleash your imagination! Drop by our website to learn more about our games or make purchases from our online store. Also available in comic book and game stores everywhere.

www.palladiumbooks.com

—a possible 80% of the population—

—would have voted for the Communist Ho Chi Minh as their leader. They see him as their George Washington. In fact, he admires George Washington—

ZPFF —White persons threw bottles, stones and firecrackers at 450 Negro and white demonstrators.

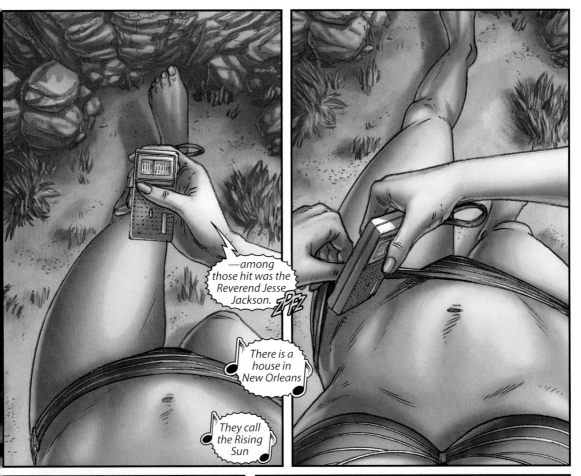

—among those hit was the Reverend Jesse Jackson. *ZPEZ*

♪ There is a house in New Orleans

♪ They call the Rising Sun

♪ It's been the ruin of many a poor girl

—from Japan are now on exhibit at the *ZZZ*

Now, at the time I was working a lot of different jobs,

I had an internship, and then I worked as a waitress.

going from one job to the next.

I woke up at like 4 or 5 in the morning,

and I was breathing heavy, sort of panting—

—and sweating, I felt like I was being chased or something like that.

My body was just sort of freaking out.

I didn't know what it was.

As I was waking up, I sort of abesentmindedly, as one will do—

LIFEGUARD ON DUTY

I was running very late one day,

so I pull into the garage in my car, throw my uniform, which was still in my car from the night before, into the wash, run up to my apartment, and I'm thinking, "OK, here's what I can do:

I can either change my clothes, put on pants and a shirt, go all the way back downstairs,

through the garage, through the laundry room, get my clothes—

—then run all the way back upstairs to my apartment, change—

VALIANT | THE STORY STARTS HERE

DISCOVER THE LARGEST INDEPENDENT SUPERHERO UNIVERSE
IN COMICS | EACH VOLUME ONE ONLY $9.99

THE VALIANT

X-O MANOWAR
VOL. 1: BY THE SWORD

BLOODSHOT REBORN
VOL. 1: COLORADO

HARBINGER
VOL. 1: OMEGA RISING

DIVINITY

QUANTUM AND WOODY
VOL. 1: THE WORLD'S WORST
SUPERHERO TEAM

THE DEATH-DEFYING
DR. MIRAGE

RAI
VOL. 1: WELCOME TO NEW JAPAN

NINJAK
VOL. 1: WEAPONEER

ARCHER & ARMSTRONG
VOL. 1: THE MICHELANGELO CODE

IVAR, TIMEWALKER
VOL. 1: MAKING HISTORY

IMPERIUM
VOL. 1: COLLECTING MONSTER

VALIANTUNIVERSE.COM | FB.COM/VALIANTCOMICS | TWITTER.COM/VALIANTCOMICS | #VALIANT

Skies are clear, it's 76 degrees—

—in Pittsburgh at this hour, and now—

—the latest news from the station that's first on your dial—

—KBRF 530.

Where'd they...

...all go...?

Wait...Don't go under!

Eye-witnesses say that they are

ordinary looking people who appear to be—

—in some kind of a trance—

GET HELP!

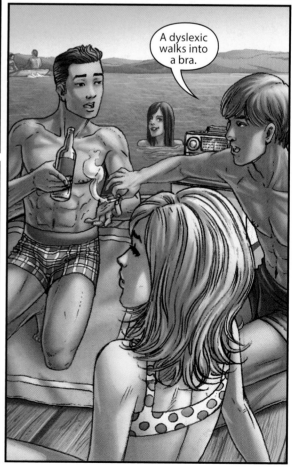

Beautiful day.

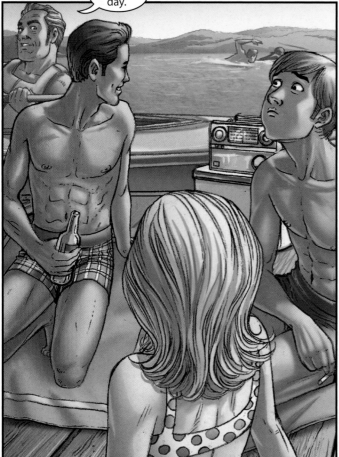

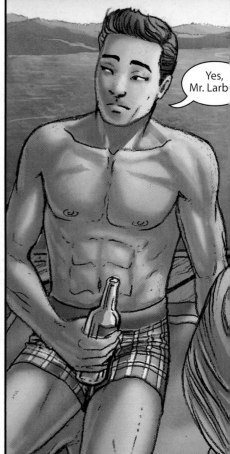

Yes, Mr. Larb

Hey, kids.

Hello, Mr. Larber.

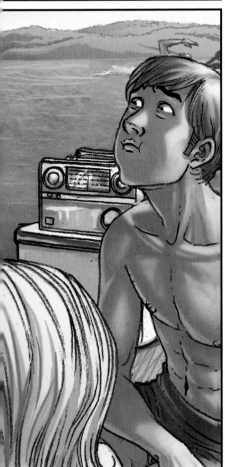

"But we need to go to the emergency room."

At that moment, my father, the Marine, the Korea Vet,

the DA who tangles with major crime families,

completely loses his cool.

His first instinct is to go look at it—

Rob?

HELP!

FWEEEET

My husband's gone!!

Out of—

What the...?

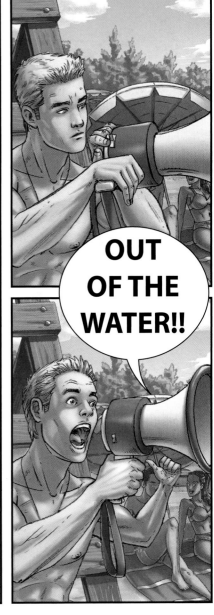

OUT OF THE WATER!!

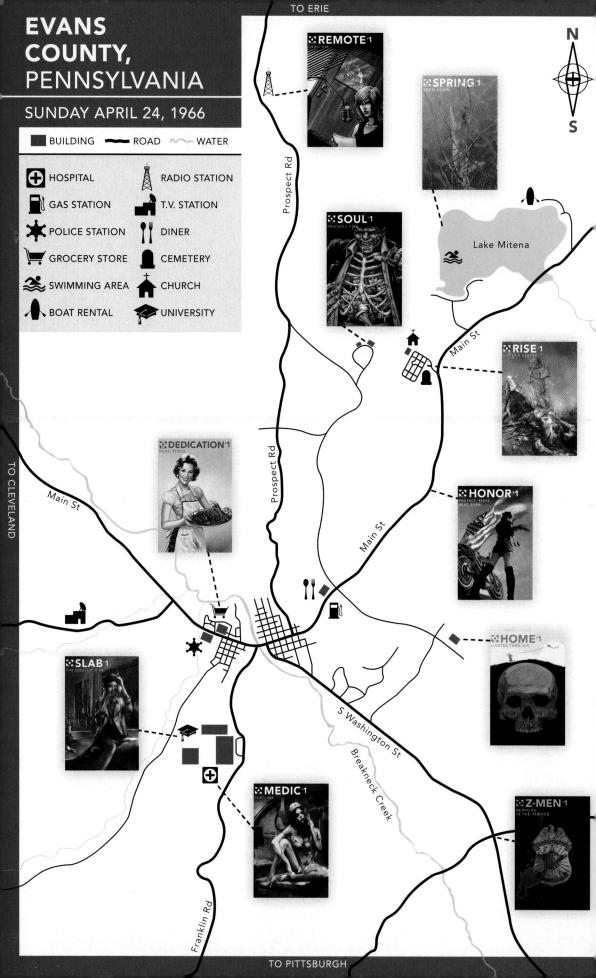

THANK YOU
FOR YOUR CONTRIBUTIONS, COLLABORATION, AND SUPPORT.

Strauss Zelnick

Hao Zheng

Dwight Zimmerman

Billy Yocum

Butch & Susan Yocum

Jerry Wang

Peter Welch

Heather Werber

Adam Wexler

Mitchell Wojcik

Michael Worosz

Bob Wulff

Teodora Varga

Jean Vargas

John Taddeo

David & Jean Tan

Rebecca Tan

Jamie Tanner

Jude Terror

Peter Thomatos

Zac Thompson

April Salazar

Darren Sanchez

Sam Saxton

Cassandra Schaffa

Gareb Shamus

Klaus Shmidheiser

Cori Silberman

Jeffrey Simons

Karl Slatoff

Mat Smart

Catherine Smyka

Jay Spence

Kingston Stafford

Lili Stiefel

Sage Stossel

Ethan Rasiel

Mike Rivera

John Roberts

John Robinson

Hans Rodionoff

Mike Rosenzweig

Sharon & Blake Rowe

Emmanuel Ogwang

Dino Pai

Ron Perazza

Rock Persaud

Fred Pierce

Amanda Proscia

Qui Nguyen

Nicole Nicoletti

Jai Nitz

Ralph Macchio

Max MacDonald

Brian David Marshall

Mike Martucci

Michael Meyers

Peter Milligan

Jane Milrod

Tom Mitchell

Randy Monkarsh

Michaela Murphy

Tony Lee

Ken Levine

Josh Leuze

Alan Lewis

Ping Liang

Stephen Liang

Gui Karyo

Jordan Katz

Maria Jagodka

Rose & Bill Jemas

Orissa Jenkins

Rich Johnston

Dan Jolly

Justin Jordan

Alex Hamby

Harry Haramis

Daniel Heacox

Daniel & Hyo Nam Heller

Krystof & Krystal Heller

Young Ai Heller

Peter Herrmann

Keith Hilber

Matt Hoverman

Darren Hutchinson

Daniel Gallina

Court Gebeau

Hayley Geftman-Gold

Greg Gibson

Flinn Gillan

David Macho Gómez

Sarah Gordon

Andrew Granik

Bobby Graves

Robert Graves

Robin Murphy Graves

Kathryn Greenbaum

John Greenbaum

John Falco

Adam Fenton

Christopher Fiumano

Claire Flanagan

Fiona Flanagan

Nancy & Tim Flanagan

Teresa Focarille

Drew Ford

Atom Freeman

Chris Eaton

Otto Eckstein

Carter Edwards

Daniel Einzig

Howard Emanuel

Vonnetta Ewing

Kathleen Davis

Shawn DeLoache

Kimberly Devaney

Gavin Dillinger

Mike Dolce

Stan & Janet Dranginis

Lucas Duimstra

Christian Cafiero

Jason Calvert

Peter Carbonaro

Chris Casazza

Skye Chalmers

Ben Chamberlain

Larry Charlip

Muhammad Chaudhry

Stephanie Chu

Brian Clevinger

Bill & Mary Coast

David Cox

Maria Barreras

Peter Begler

Ian Berry

Cheryl & Larry Bishop

Ralph Blaser

Siobhan Boes

Tommy Bolduc

Phil Boyle

Maya Bronfman

Juliette Brooks

Gahl Buslov

Tony Buttino

Jared Atchison

Chris Arrant

Christle Arriola

Tisha Ayala

Ellen Dranginis

Antoine Boisvert

KB Breiseth

All of us here, at Double Take admire and respect the creators, cast and crew, of the 1968 film *Night of the Living Dead.* While no one affiliated with the film has been involved in the creation of these stories, their wonderful work inspired us.

SID MEIER'S CIVILIZATION®
BEYOND EARTH™

WWW.CIVILIZATION.COM

SLAB #1

THE DOCTOR IS IN

JBLE TAKE

$2.50

FINKELSTEIN | JEMAS | ROWE | COAST | COOPER